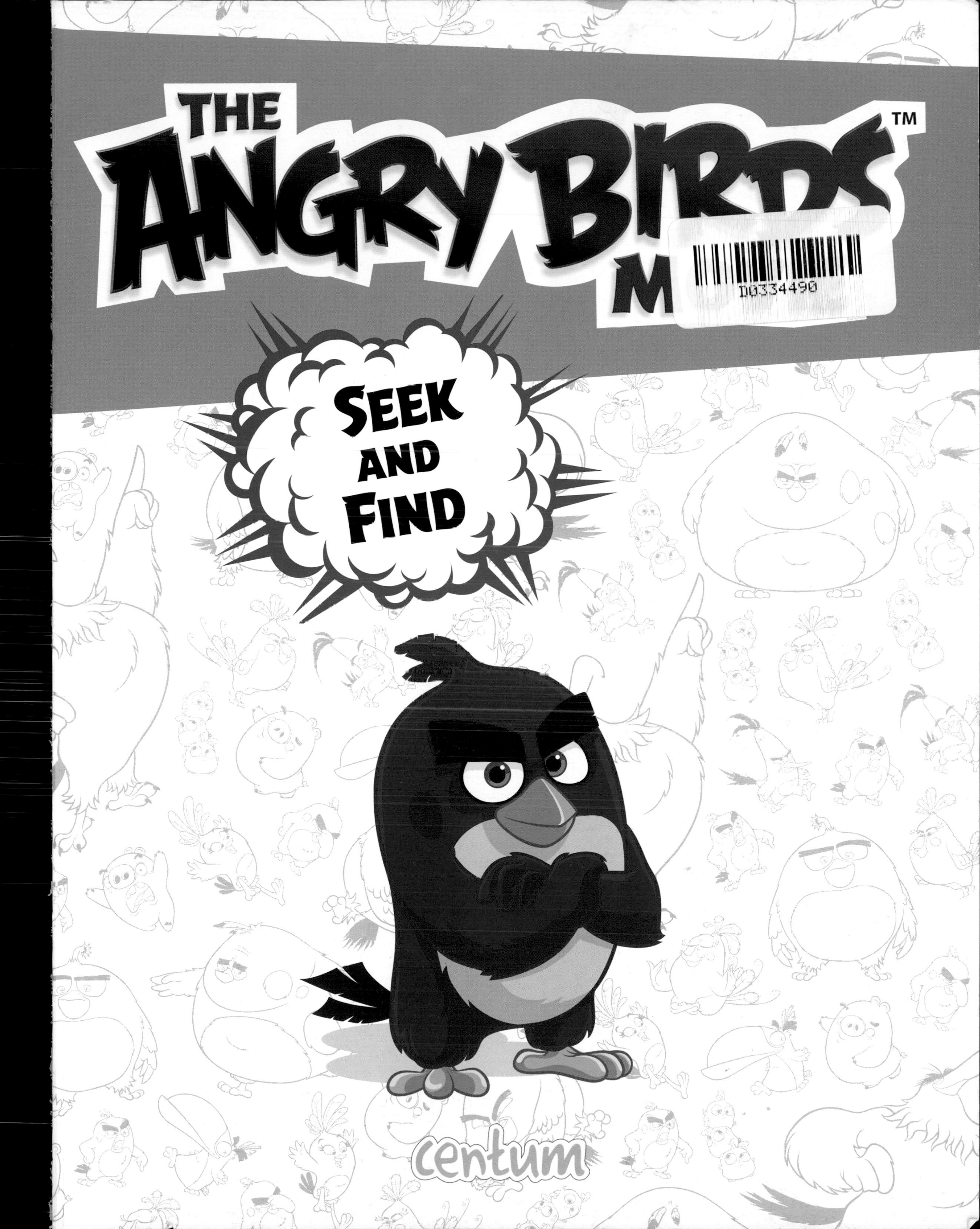
THE
ANGRY BIRDS
M
™
SEEK AND FIND
centum

THE ANGRY BIRDS MOVIE: SEEK AND FIND

A CENTUM BOOK ISBN: 978-1-910917-14-5

Published in Great Britain by Centum Books Ltd

Centum Books Ltd, 20 Devon Square, Newton Abbot, Devon, TQ12 2HR, UK

books@centumbooksltd.co.uk

CENTUM BOOKS Limited Reg. No. 07641486

This edition published 2016

A CIP catalogue record for this book is available from the British Library

Printed in China.

1 3 5 7 9 10 8 6 4 2

Welcome, Feathered Friend!

You're about to embark on a journey of discovery - quite literally! Using all your powers of deduction, The Angry Birds challenge you to search for the many hidden items in this book. Will you find them all?

To help you on your search, read these red-hot tips from the Angry Birds:

It's very important to stay calm at ALL times. You won't find anything if you're frantically searching around a page.

Take deep breaths. This will help you relax and focus your mind on the job in hand.

At some point you might feel like giving up. If you can't find something, there's no shame in leaving it and coming back to it later. Don't be in a rush!

Whatever you do, don't get distracted by pigs. Pigs are very distracting. And annoying. In fact they are the most annoying things in the history of annoying things.

LET'S BEGIN...

It's time to flex those eye sockets in this warm-up puzzle. Get ready, set, SEARCH!

Find the four hidden letters that spell out an angry word.

A

G

CAN YOU FIND?
One speeding Chuck
One angry Bomb
One silly pig
One flying Red
One Mighty Eagle that's different

Bird Village

Red needs some new tools so he can fix up his beloved home. Unfortunately his shopping trip is turning into a bit of nightmare as there are birds and pigs everywhere! Help him find the things he needs so he can get back home as quickly as possible.

FRUIT

EARLY BIRD WORMS
WORMS
NAP BAR
CAN YOU FIND?
Nuts x3
Bolts x3
Spanner
Screwdriver
Glue
Hammer
Find the five hidden letters that spell out what Red would like to be right now.

FEELING SQUARE
This puzzle might just drive you crazy, nearly as crazy as the pigs make Red!
CAN YOU FIND?
A Red with green eyes
A Blue that's green
A pig with no teeth
A yellow-beaked Mighty Eagle
A tiny-faced Terence

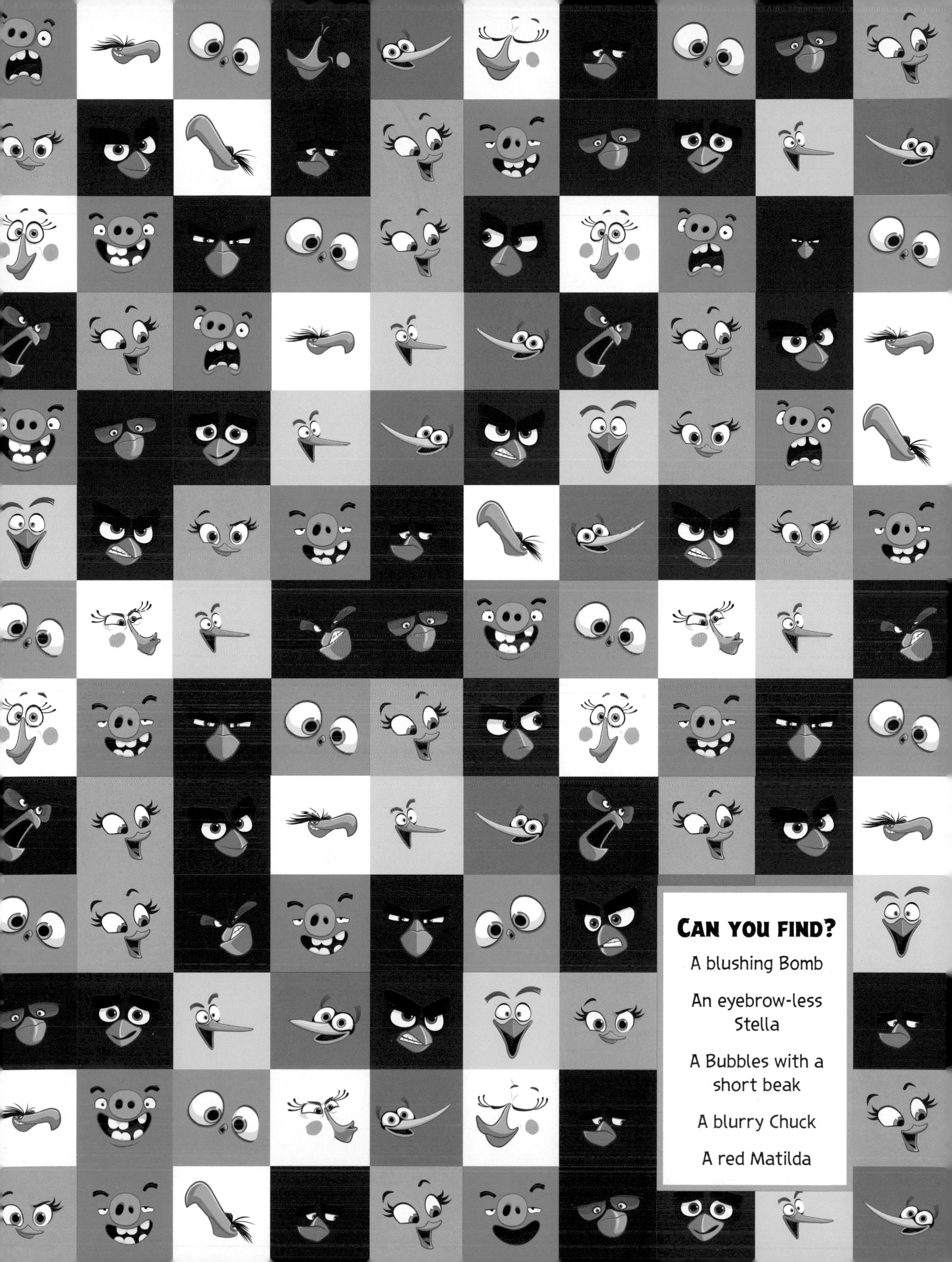
CAN YOU FIND?
A blushing Bomb
An eyebrow-less Stella
A Bubbles with a short beak
A blurry Chuck
A red Matilda

Dinner for One

Poor Red, all he wants is some peace and quiet so he can enjoy his delicious dinner for one. Instead he's sat in the middle of a feeding frenzy!

MENU

CAN YOU FIND?
A lollipop
A cookie
An apple
A watermelon slice
A plate of seed
A doughnut
A sandwich
A bone
A bunch of blueberries
A plate of spaghetti
Menu
There are ten bananas in this scene, can you find them all?

CLOUDS OF RAGE!
Uh-oh, you know what time it is. Red has got his rage on, he's so furious that he might get himself into trouble with Judge Peckinpah. Can you calm him down by solving this puzzle?
Find seven letters that spell out a word that Red tends to do a lot.

CAN YOU FIND?
Five rage-fuelled skulls
Five explosive thunder clouds

BIG TROUBLE
Judge Peckinpah has only one way of dealing with this angry bird, and that's to send him to Anger Management Class. Who else is here for Red's day of reckoning?

CAN YOU FIND?
The Judge's hat
Judge's hammer
Handcuffs
Siren
Sheriff badge
Some red feathers
Fireman's hat
Policeman's hat
Quill and ink
Typewriter
Find five hidden letters that spell out a very important word.

FEATHERED FURY
Red does ruffle a few feathers. In fact he's been ruffling feathers since he was a hatchling. That's a lot of feathers! This puzzle might ruffle yours, just try and stay calm.

CAN YOU FIND?
The smallest feather
The biggest feather
This fancy feather
This leaf
This flower
Five of these feathers:
Find three hidden letters that spell out a word that's very calming.

Anger Management

Another day, another Anger Management Class with Matilda – the master of meditation. Red's unsure about all this Zen stuff, he'd much rather be fixing up his home – ALONE! What can you spot in this calming scene?

Can You Find?
Five incense sticks
Five smelly candles
Find four hidden letters that spell a relaxing word.

PIG INVASION!

Ah! Have you ever seen pages so green? There are pigs everywhere. Big pigs, little pigs and mini pigs!

Can You Find?
The twenty mini pigs
Find four hidden letters that spell out a word the pigs love!

PIGGY PARTY!

The pigs love to eat, sleep and build, but they also LOVE to dress up. Here is a rare and exciting glimpse into their costume cupboard where all sorts of fun and frolics happen!

Find four hidden letters that spell out a word that the pigs love to do!
DIY
CAN YOU FIND?
Pink glasses
Red heart-shaped glasses
Yellow star-shaped glasses
Orange moustache
Pink feather bower
White top hat
Black mask
Purple wig
Green roller skates
Magnificent pink cape
TNT

The Mighty Lair

The birds love their hero Mighty Eagle, although not as much as this eagle loves himself. His lair is full of mighty memorabilia. What can you spot here?

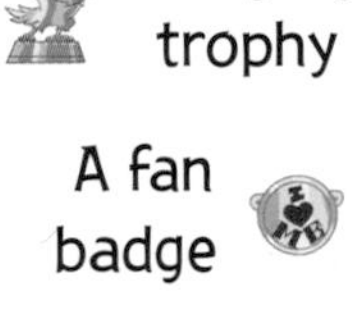

Can you Find?

- A cactus
- A football
- Feather grooming oil
- A telescope
- Mighty Eagle comic
- A mighty trophy
- A fan badge
- A beauty mask
- A mighty flag
- A rubber ring

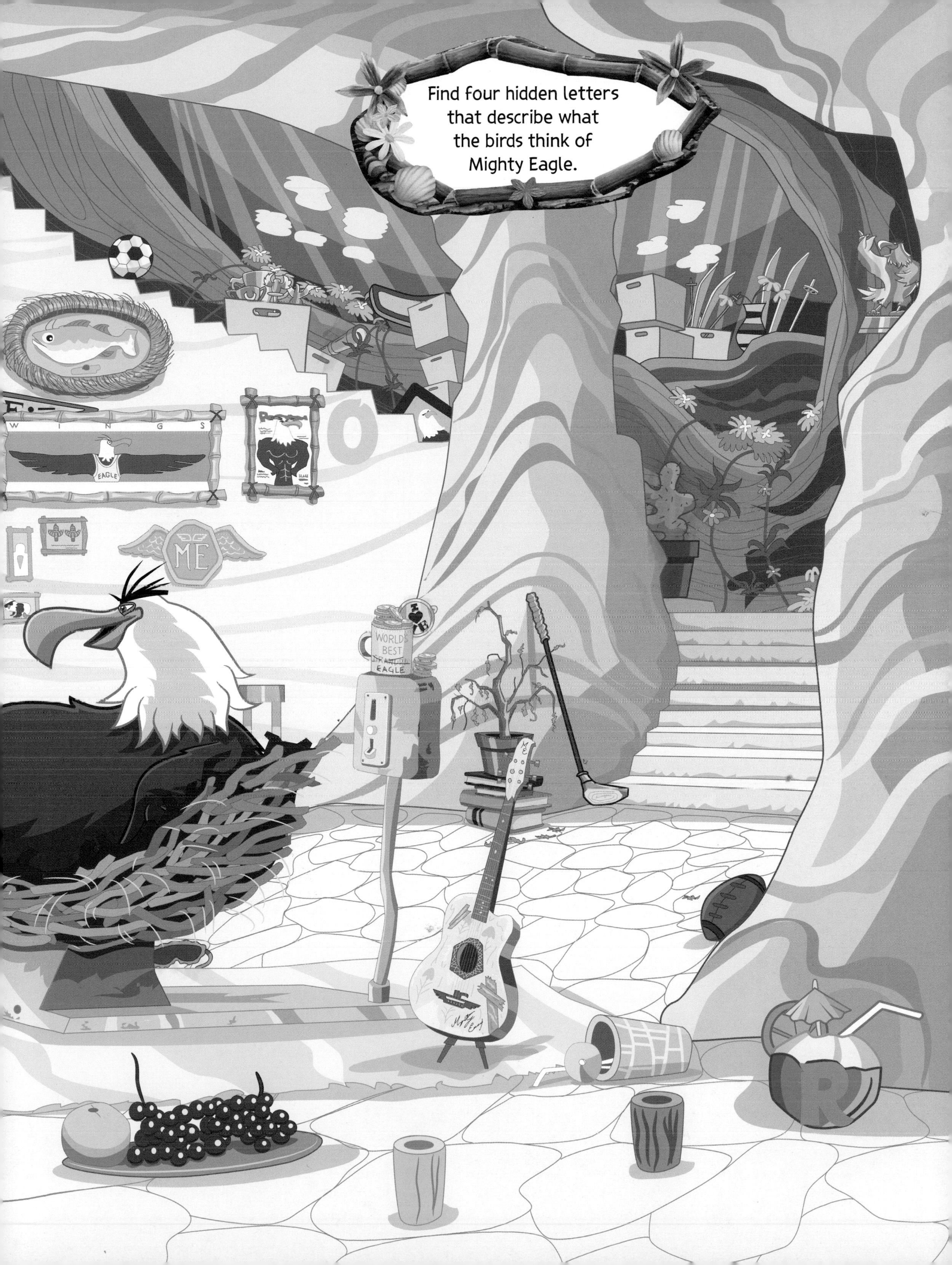

Find four hidden letters that describe what the birds think of Mighty Eagle.

THE RACE OF RAGE
The Angry Birds are racing to Pig Island to rescue the eggs that the pigs have stolen. Fuelled by rage, help these birds speed through the grid following the correct sequence and save the day!
START
You cannot travel diagonally!

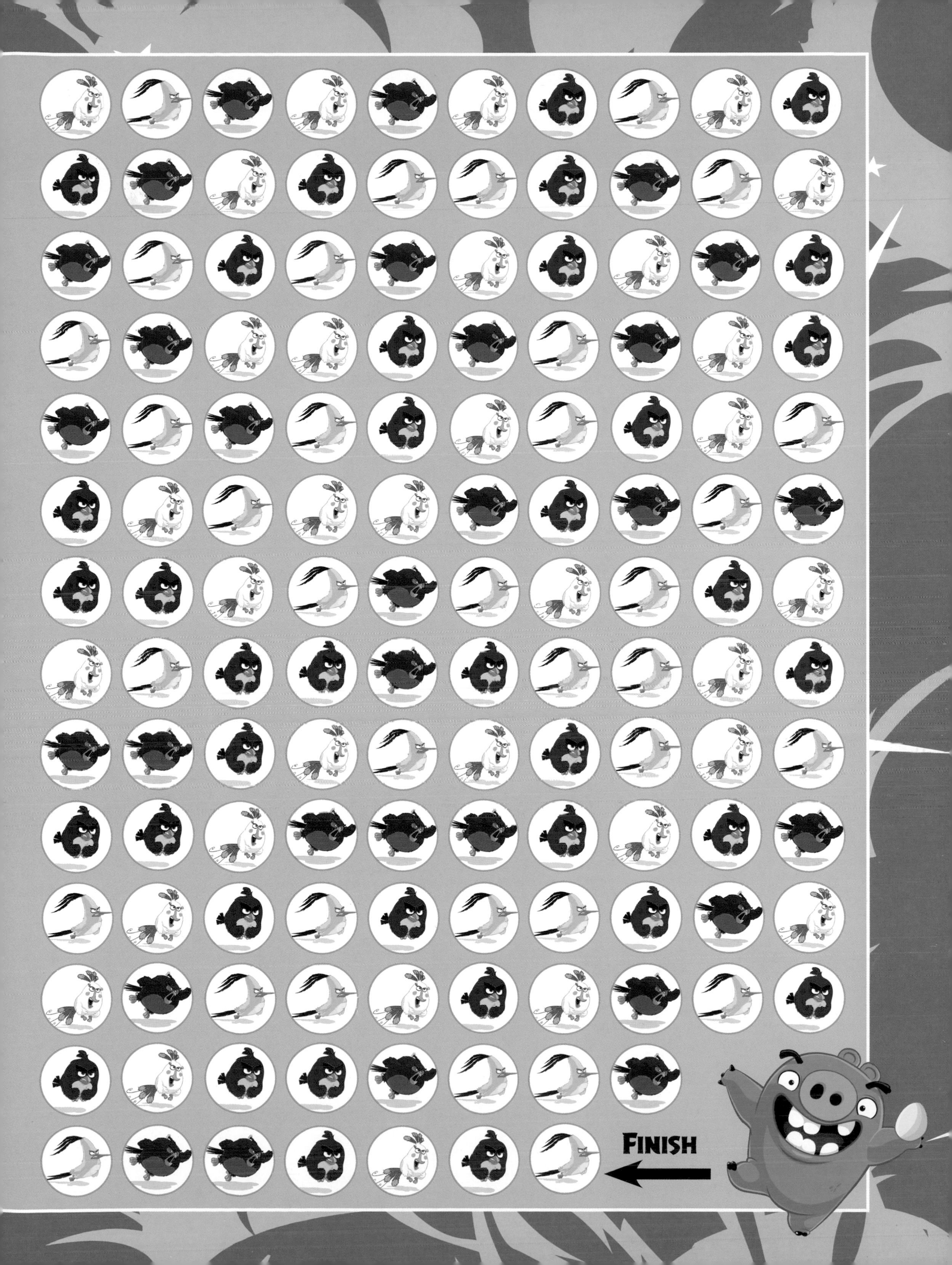
FINISH

Pig City

What a busy place Pig City is – full of many amazing sights, sounds and smells. Mostly smells. The pigs think they have got away with stealing the birds' eggs, but one very red and very angry bird is here to take them back.

Can you Find?

- Ten yellow eggs
- Four hot dogs
- Flying goggles
- A bicycle helmet
- A newspaper
- A whistle
- A piggy camera
- A pig-shaped balloon

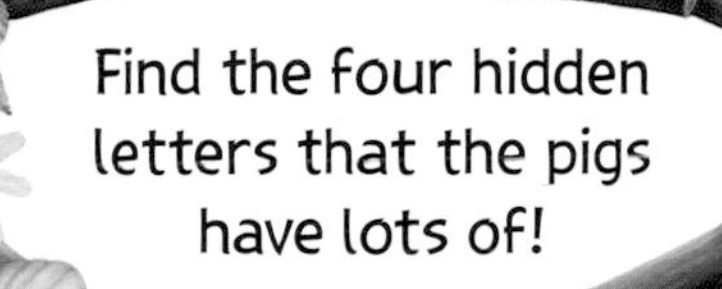
Find the four hidden letters that the pigs have lots of!

ANSWERS

DINNER FOR ONE

LET'S BEGIN . . .

The hidden word is RAGE

CLOUDS OF RAGE!

The hidden word is EXPLODE

BIRD VILLAGE

The hidden word is ALONE

BIG TROUBLE

The hidden word is JUDGE

FEELING SQUARE

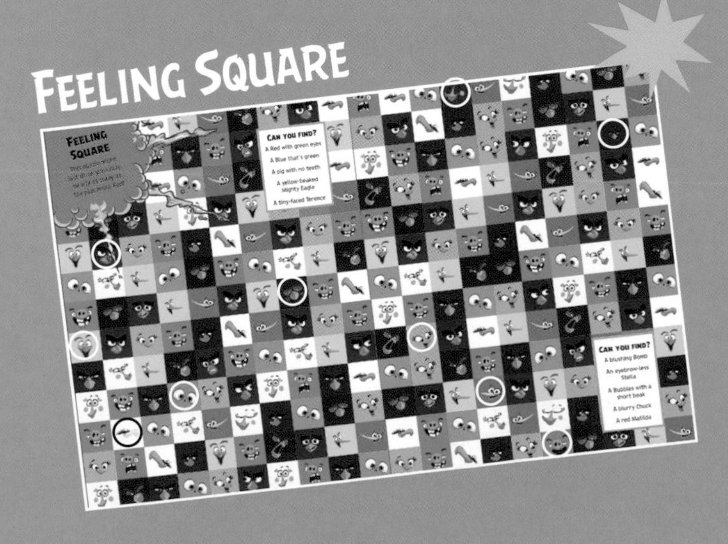

Feathered Fury

The hidden word is ZEN

The Mighty Lair

The hidden word is HERO

Anger Management

The hidden word is CALM

Pig Invasion!

The hidden word is EGGS

The Race of Rage

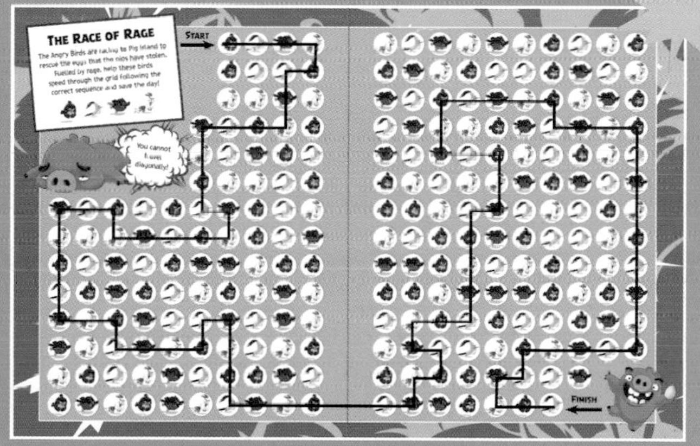

Pig City

The hidden word is FOOD

Piggy Party!

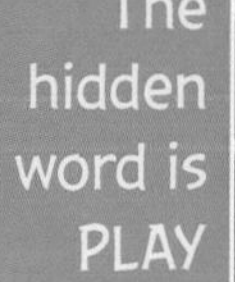

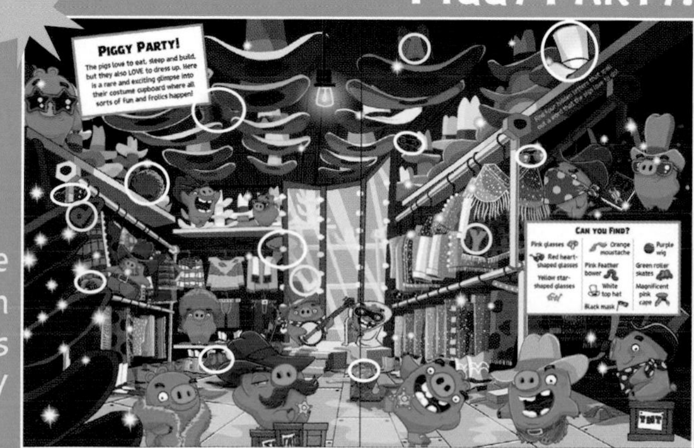

The hidden word is PLAY

EGG-STRA ITEMS TO SEEK

Can you find these EGGS-tra special items hidden throughout the book? If you can't find them then read the clues to help narrow down your search.

1) Mighty Eagle's autographed pictures

2) Bomb's singed party hat

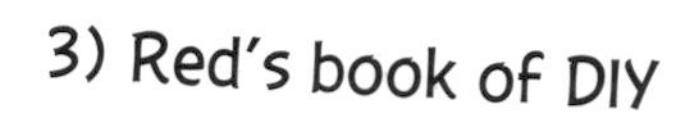

3) Red's book of DIY

4) Terence's heart-shaped mirror

5) Ross's slingshot

6) King Pig's crown

7) Judge Peckinpah's old spectacles

8) Bubbles' noisy horn

9) Leonard's beard grooming brush

10) Matilda's yoga mat

Have you got what it takes to find the giant golden egg?

CLUES

Here are some clues to help you if you need it!

1) Look in Bird Court. 2) Take another look at Anger Management Class. 3) Piggy Party is the place. 4) It's around Mighty Eagle's Lair. 5) Anger Management Class is a good start. 6) Pig City – go look! 7) Seek them in the restaurant scene. 8) Why don't you go shopping? 9) Look around the Pig City. 10) Something tells me it's in Anger Management Class. The giant golden egg is hidden in the restaurant scene – did you find it?